W9-CBS-603

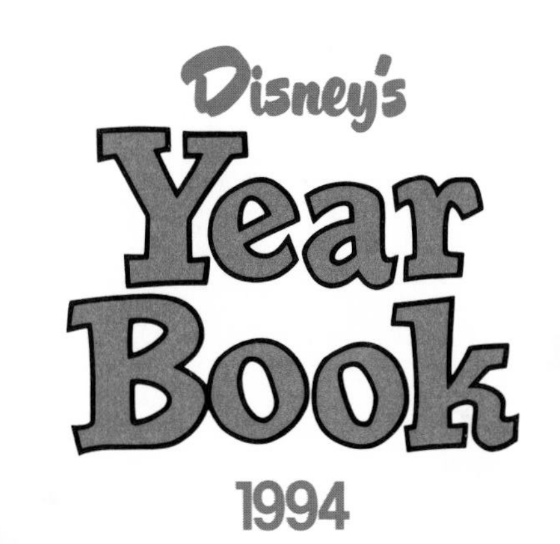
Disney's
Year
Book
1994

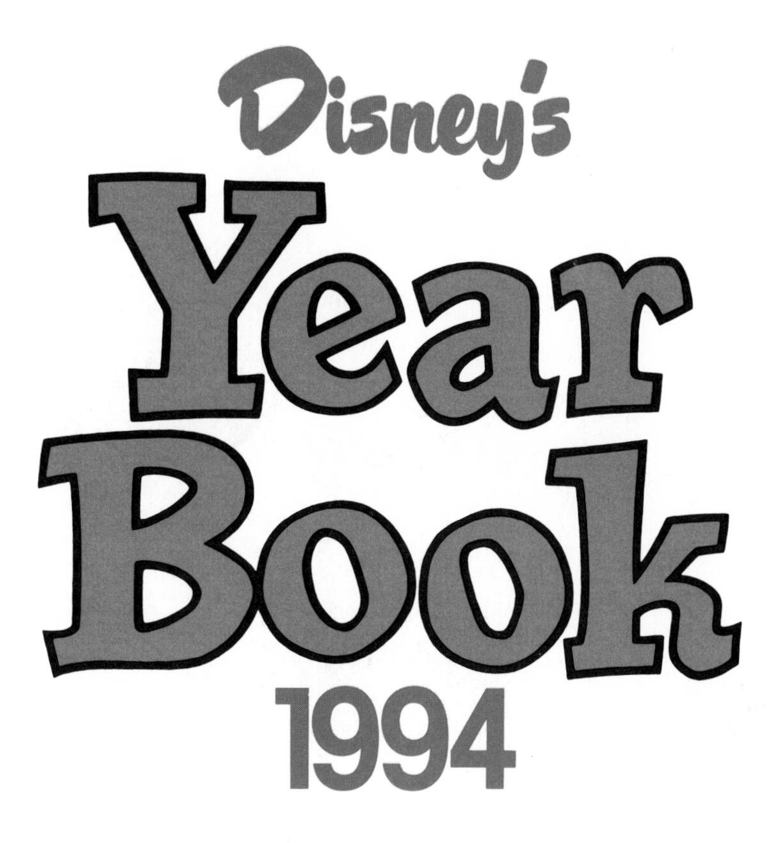

GROLIER ENTERPRISES INC.
Danbury, Connecticut

FERN L. MAMBERG *Executive Editor*
ELIZABETH A. FARRINGTON *Art Director*
HARRIETT GREYSTONE *Production Manager*

ISBN: 0-7172-8341-0
ISSN: 0273-1274

Stories on pages 14–25, 36–47, 54–65, 72–83, and all Disney character illustrations copyright © 1994 by The Walt Disney Company

Copyright © 1994 by Grolier Incorporated

No part of this book may be reproduced without special permission in writing from the publishers

PRINTED IN THE UNITED STATES OF AMERICA

Illustration Credits and Acknowledgments

6—© James Lemass/Gamma-Liaison; © Chris Luneski/Image Cascade; 7—The Chicago Historical Society; 8–9—© Chris Luneski/Image Cascade; 10–11—© C. & S. Politt/Australasian Nature Transparencies; 12—© Hans & Judy Beste/Animals Animals; 13—© John Everingham; © Dave Watts/Australasian Nature Transparencies; 26—© Tom & Deeann McCarthy/The Stock Market; 27—Artist, Tom Barrett; 28—© John McGrail; © Charles Phillips; 29—© J. Barry O'Rourke/The Stock Market; 48—© Gregory G. Dimijian/Photo Researchers, Inc.; © Rod Williams/Bruce Coleman, Inc.; 81—Densey Clyne/Oxford Scientific Films/Animals Animals; © K. G. Preston-Mafham/Animals Animals; 50—© Gail Mooney; 51—Artist, Michèle A. McLean; 52–53—© Gail Mooney; 66—© Allan Tannenbaum/Sygma; 67—The Granger Collection; UPI/Bettmann; 68—UPI/Bettmann; © Ken Hawkins/Sygma; 69—© Mike Marucci/Sipa; 70–71—Designed and created by Jenny Tesar; 84—© Breck P. Kent/Animals Animals; © Kathie Atkinson/Animals Animals; 85—Ronald J. Larson; © Andrew Martinez/Photo Researchers, Inc.; © Ronald J. Larson; 86—© Kathleen S. Larson; 87—© David Thompson/Animals Animals; 88—AP/Wide World Photos; 89—© Bill Rowe/Picture Group; © Haviv/Saba; 91—© Haviv/Saba; 92—© Mickey Pfleger; © Richard Faverty; 93—© Mickey Pfleger; 94—© Phil Schermeister; 94–95—© Richard Faverty; 95—© Richard Faverty

Contents

Pleasure Wheels

Step aboard and ride the "pleasure wheel!" As the wheel begins to turn, it sweeps you up, up into the sky. You gaze down. There, spread out below you, is all the excitement of a fair, carnival, or amusement park. And beyond the fair are fabulous views of the countryside.

Pleasure wheels, as they were once called, have been around for hundreds of years. But today these rides are known as Ferris wheels. They were named after a gigantic wheel that was set up at the 1893 World's Fair in Chicago, Illinois. And in 1993, people all over the world celebrated the 100th anniversary of the invention of the Ferris wheel.

The basic idea of this wonderful amusement ride is simple: People ride in cars hanging from a giant wheel. What, then, was so special about the wheel that was built for the Chicago fair? How was it different from the earlier pleasure wheels? Well, the people who organized that fair wanted to build something that would outshine the Eiffel Tower—which was an engineering marvel that had been built for the Paris Exposition of 1889. George Ferris, a bridge

This postcard shows the first Ferris wheel, at the 1893 Chicago World's Fair.

builder, said he could build them a gigantic pleasure wheel with a diameter of 250 feet—much, much bigger than any other pleasure wheel up to that time. It would have 36 cars, each with 40 chairs. Some people laughed: "Ferris is a crackpot. He has wheels in his head!" But Ferris convinced them that his wheel would work, and that it would be safe.

Construction began in January 1893. Eight deep holes were dug in the ground and filled with concrete and steel. On these foundations were bolted two steel towers, each 140 feet tall. A giant axle was hoisted between the towers. The crew then assembled the wheel around the axle and attached the cars to the wheel. Two giant steam engines were used to turn the wheel.

The Ferris wheel opened on June 21 and quickly became the Chicago fair's most sensational attraction.

Take a zip on the Zipper, a hair-raising ride that will turn you upside down.

While one wheel of the double Ferris wheel is near the ground being filled with passengers, the other revolves high in the air.

By the time the fair closed at the end of October, more than 1.5 million people had taken rides on it.

Ferris's wheel inspired other builders. They made smaller wheels that could easily be taken down, transported, and reassembled at different fairs. Most modern Ferris wheels are about 50 feet in diameter, and each car carries just two people.

In addition to the standard Ferris wheel design, there have been many different spin-offs. One is the double Ferris wheel. It looks like a seesaw, with a central hub and two wheels. Other wheels have been built for super thrills. Among them is the Zipper, which moves two-passenger cages up into the air along an oval track. The cages swing, tip, and turn upside down.

The Ferris wheel still delights happily screaming people of all ages. It continues to spin 'round and 'round as it begins a second century of providing amusement at fairs around the world.

KOALAS: Like Living Toys

With its plump, pear-shaped body, sleepy eyes, big ears, and thick cuddly fur, the koala is one of the cutest animals in the world. Koalas almost look more like stuffed toys than real animals. They are so beloved by people everywhere that they are considered a national symbol in their homeland of Australia.

Koalas are good-tempered animals that look like little bears. But they aren't bears at all. They are marsupials—mammals that raise their young in pouches outside the body.

KOALA QUIPS

- *The koala was given its name by the aborigines, or native Australians.* Koala *means "drink no water."*
- *Koalas sometimes eat dirt, which may provide minerals or help them digest eucalyptus leaves.*
- *Koalas make many different sounds. Males grunt like pigs, while females make a higher-pitched noise. Frightened koalas howl and wail, and the cries of lost baby koalas sound like the cries of human babies. Groups of koalas have even been heard murmuring to each other in the trees.*

Koalas spend most of their lives in eucalyptus trees. The leaves from these trees provide them with food. And they are expert climbers. They have long, sharp claws, and their hands and feet are great for grasping tree branches. Koalas rarely go down to the ground. If necessary, they can leap as much as three feet to reach a new tree. On the ground, koalas waddle along and can be attacked by predators. But as long as there are enough eucalyptus leaves, there is little need for a koala to go down to the ground.

Young koalas are born singly (twins are very rare) about 35 days after mating. A koala is the size of a lima bean at birth, and it is

Koala Chow

A koala's diet is made up almost entirely of eucalyptus leaves—but not just any *eucalyptus leaves! There are more than 600 different kinds of eucalyptus in Australia. However, koalas eat leaves from only about thirty kinds. They seldom if ever drink water—they get all the moisture they need from the leaves.*

blind and hairless. It immediately crawls into its mother's pouch and attaches itself to a teat. There it stays, sucking milk and growing into a furry young koala. After about seven months, the koala leaves the pouch for good. It rides around on its mother's back, learning to eat leaves and clamber around in the trees, until it is about a year old. Then it becomes more independent. When a koala is about eighteen months old, it usually leaves to find its own territory. Except during the mating season, koalas tend to live alone. In the wild, they usually live about twelve years, but they can live to be twenty or more.

Today there are about 400,000 koalas throughout eastern Australia. But their number is declining. They are a threatened

A baby koala rides on its mother's back for about a year.

species. One reason for this is that their eucalyptus forests have been cut down to make way for homes and farms. Australians are now helping the koalas. They are trying, for example, to develop a diet

to replace eucalyptus leaves. And they are also studying several ways to preserve koala habitats. Australians want to be sure that the cuddly koala will always be around for the world to love.

Koalas can spend twenty hours a day sleeping snugly in the fork of a tree.

CHIP AND LITTLE CHEEP

One cold fall day, Chip wandered through the castle. All the other Enchanted Objects were hard at work. But Chip couldn't find anything to do.

In the kitchen, Mrs. Potts and the stove were frosting a cake. "Let me help, Mama!" Chip exclaimed. But when he tried to stir the frosting, it splashed all over.

"Oh, dear, Chip," Mrs. Potts sighed as she wiped his face. "You're too little to help with the baking. Run along and find something else to do."

Chip trudged out of the kitchen and into the hallway. He saw Cogsworth standing on a ladder, dusting the suits of armor.

"Let me help!" Chip said. He picked up a dustcloth and climbed up the ladder next to Cogsworth. Chip began to rub as hard as he could. He rubbed so hard, the armor started to shake and sway back and forth.

"Don't rub so hard!" Cogsworth cried. But it was too late. The armor began to tilt. Then it fell. *Clang!* Down went the armor, knocking the ladder over. Down went Cogsworth and Chip. The armor's helmet landed on top of Chip.

"Dear, dear," Cogsworth said, opening the helmet visor and peering in at Chip. "You're too little for this job, Chip. Run along and find something else to do." He lifted the helmet off Chip and sent him on his way.

Chip was very embarrassed. He scooted down the hall and into the dining room.

Lumiere was lighting candles on the dining table.

"I want to help!" Chip said.

But as he hopped across the table toward Lumiere, Chip knocked over the water pitcher. Water splashed all over Lumiere and put out the candles on the table. “My, my,” Lumiere said, shaking himself dry. “I don’t think you can help me here. Run along and find something else to do.”

Now Chip was discouraged. As he wandered past the library, he saw Belle carrying a big stack of books. Surely Belle would let him help her! But as Chip rushed into the library, he tripped on the edge of a rug and went flying through the air.

"Chip, watch out!" Belle cried. She dropped the books and caught him in her hands. "Oh, my, you gave me a scare!" Belle said, putting Chip down. Books were scattered everywhere.

"I wanted to help, but I made you drop the books," Chip said sadly.

"It doesn't matter," Belle answered. "I can pick them up. They're much too heavy for you to lift anyway. Why don't you run along outside and find something else to do?"

Feeling very small and very sad, Chip trudged out of the library into the garden.

It was chilly and damp outside. Chip shivered as he walked along the garden path. "Everyone thinks I'm too little to help," he said to himself. "Maybe they're right."

Just then, Chip heard a small peeping noise. It sounded like someone was crying. Chip looked around.

There was a tiny bird lying on the ground. When it saw Chip, the little bird blinked its shiny black eyes and cried.

"What's the matter?" Chip asked. The little bird ruffled its feathers and opened and closed its orange beak.

"Maybe you're thirsty," Chip said. He hurried to the garden fountain and dipped up some water. The little bird drank all the water. But then he started to cry again.

"I know. You're probably hungry!" Chip exclaimed. He hopped to the barn. Chip scooped up some yellow corn and took it to the bird. The bird ate all the corn. But then he started to cry again.

"You look cold," Chip said. "I'll make you a warm nest of leaves."

Chip started to pile leaves around the bird, but when he touched its wing, the little bird cried even louder.

Chip looked at the bird carefully. "Oh, I see what's wrong. Your wing is hurt!" Chip exclaimed. "I don't know how to fix that. But Belle can help you. I'll go get her."

But when Chip started to leave, the little bird began to cry louder than ever. It tried to follow Chip, but its hurt wing dragged along the path. After a few wobbly steps, it fell down and lay peeping sadly on the path.

"Why, you don't want me to leave you, do you?" Chip exclaimed. "But if I don't get Belle, she can't help you. Please stay here. I'll be right back." He started to walk away again, but the little bird cried louder and fluttered its hurt wing.

Chip was worried. Soon it would be night. He had to get help for the little bird. But he didn't want to leave it alone and crying.

"I know," Chip said to the little bird, "I'll carry you into the castle." Slowly Chip bent down. He carefully scooped the bird up and began to carry it up the castle steps.

"You're—whew!—bigger—oof!—than I thought!" Chip gasped as he carried the bird into the castle. Puffing and panting, Chip hurried past Cogsworth in the hall, past Lumiere in the dining room, and past Mrs. Potts in the kitchen. When they saw Chip with the bird, all the Enchanted Objects followed him into the library.

And Chip was right—Belle knew just what to do. As Chip and the others watched, she bandaged the little bird's wing. Then she made it a soft nest in a corner of the library. Soon the little bird closed its eyes and went to sleep.

Chip looked at the little bird a long time. "I wish I could help him get well," he said wistfully.

"Why, Chip, you already did!" Belle exclaimed. "You gave him water and food and carried him inside. You were the biggest help of all!"

"Not one of us could have done better," said Mrs. Potts.

Chip was beginning to feel proud of himself when the bird woke up. "Cheep! Cheep!" it called to Chip.

"Listen!" Chip exclaimed. "I think he knows I helped him."

Belle and the others smiled at Chip as he stroked the little bird's feathers. Chip looked up and smiled. "I'm going to take care of him until he's well. I'll name him 'Little Cheep,' " he said.

"Chip and Little Cheep! We'll be best friends!"

The Inside Scoop on ICE CREAM

Smooth and sweet, cool and creamy—nothing tops ice cream as a treat. In fact, ice cream and other frozen dairy desserts, such as sherbet and frozen yogurt, are so popular, they are eaten in practically every country of the world.

The idea of frozen desserts is said to have begun in the 1st century A.D. The Roman emperor Nero liked snow that was flavored with honey and fruit juices. The Chinese added milk to honey-and-fruit-flavored ices, producing something similar to

The Ice-Cream Factory

Ice cream is made in a very special way so that it is smooth and creamy. Here's how: The ice-cream mixture—milk, cream, and sugar—is prepared (1). The mix is pasteurized (2) and homogenized (3). It is then cooled (4) and flavorings are added (5). The mix is frozen and whipped (6). Other flavorings are added (7). The ice cream is put into containers (8) and hardens in a cold room (9). Then it is trucked and delivered (10).

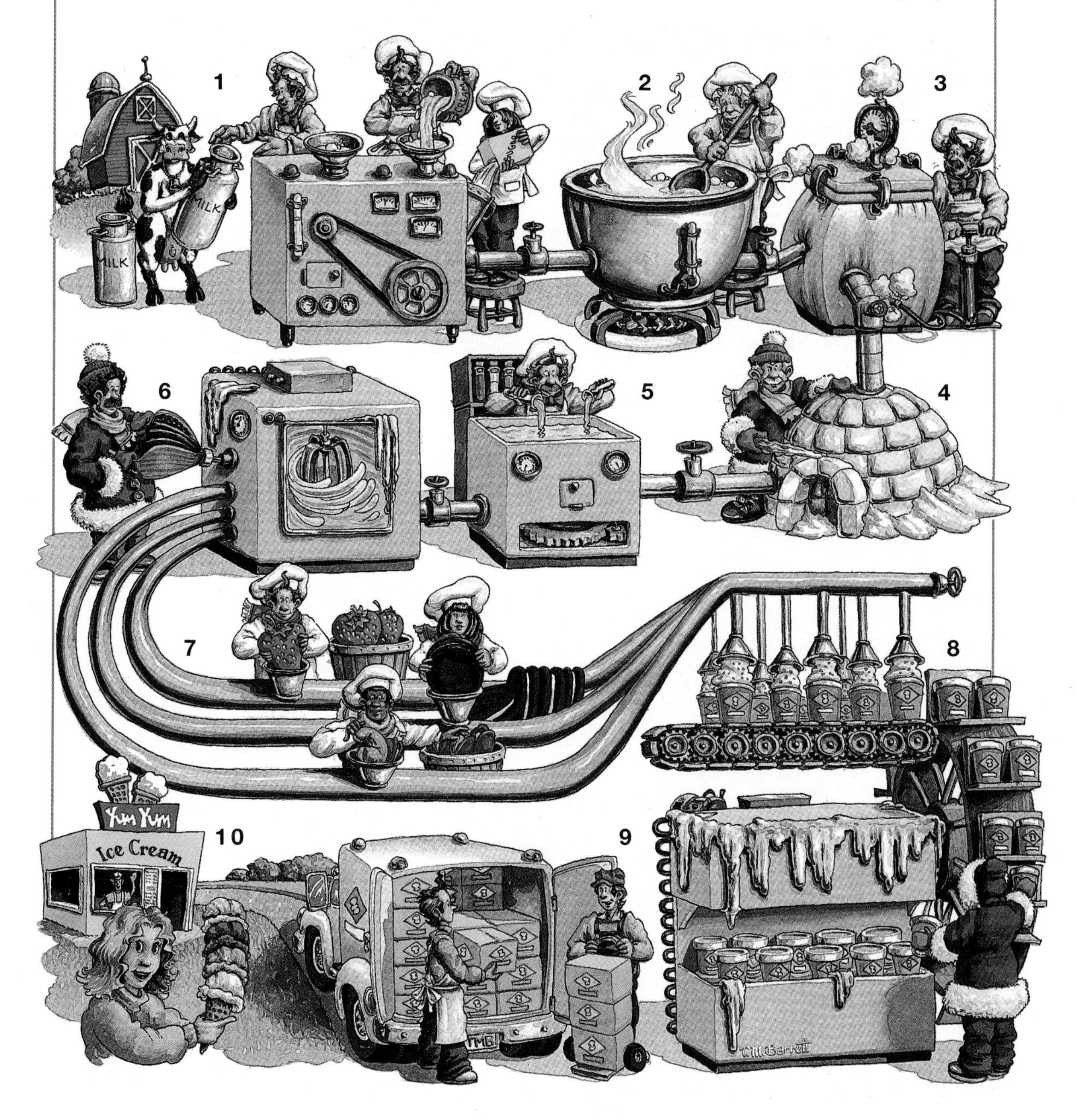

sherbet. The explorer Marco Polo brought a recipe for this Chinese sherbet back to Italy. By the 1500's the popularity of these delicious ices had spread to the rest of Europe. Later, sugar replaced honey as a sweetener, and chocolate from the New World cacao bean became a popular flavoring. Then sweetened and flavored milk replaced crushed ice—and this was the beginning of true ice cream.

Today, the most popular ice-cream flavors are vanilla, chocolate, and strawberry. But there are also such exotic flavors as bubble gum and tomato!

Tomato ice cream may not be for you. But chances are there's a flavor you adore. Almost everyone loves this cool, creamy treat.

Treat yourself to this ice-cream version of the hero sandwich—it's just layered with sweet stuff!

Yesterday's Soda Fountain

From the 1860's to the 1960's, the favorite place to enjoy ice cream was the soda fountain. Many soda fountains were in drugstores. Behind the counter, white-jacketed "soda jerks" mixed seltzer with flavored syrups. Ice cream later made its way into the mix. Soon soda fountains were creating ice-cream sodas and other ice-cream treats.

Most of these soda fountains are gone. But you can visit the old-fashioned ice-cream parlor below at the Smithsonian Institution in Washington, D.C.—and treat yourself to a Brown Cow (left), an ice-cream soda made with root beer, vanilla ice cream, and whipped cream.

MESSAGES FROM THE PAST

How would you like to visit the future and tell people who will live hundreds or thousands of years from now about your life? We can't travel through time, of course. But we can leave a special message for the future—by creating a time capsule. A time capsule is a sealed container holding items from a certain time. It may be a large chamber filled with thousands of objects. Or it may be a small box with a few personal items. Either way, the goal is to tell those who will open it what life was like in the past.

The term "time capsule" was first used to describe a 7-foot-long cigar-shaped container that was put together for the 1939 World's Fair, in New York City. Buried below the fairgrounds, the capsule was filled with dozens of common items—a toothbrush, an alarm

clock, a Bible, a safety pin, and samples of seeds, fabrics, and metals. There was also a long microfilmed essay about the culture, science, and religion of the world at that time.

> ### Your Own
> ## Time Capsule
>
> *Pretend you live in the year 2100 and find this time capsule. What would its contents tell you about today's kids?*
>
> *Here are some suggestions for making your own time capsule:*
>
> - *The contents might include a photo of yourself, a sample of your handwriting, the name of your best friend, information about your favorite book or TV show, and a newspaper from the day you bury the capsule.*
> - *If you bury your capsule outdoors, use a waterproof container, such as a large glass jar. If you hide it indoors, a cardboard box will be fine.*
> - *Decide when you will open your time capsule. Leave a note to yourself as a reminder.*

Some of the most exciting time capsules have been shot into space aboard space probes such as Voyager 1 and 2. These space-bound time capsules, carrying recordings with information about Earth, may never be seen again. But then, even time capsules that stay on Earth are never seen again either—because they are lost or forgotten. One time capsule was buried by the cast of the TV series "M*A*S*H" in 1983, in a secret ceremony. It's under a Hollywood studio parking lot . . . somewhere!

NOW YOU SEE IT... NOW YOU DON'T

Sometimes the brain "sees" things that aren't really there. Look at the drawings on these pages. Each of them tries to trick your brain!

Which blue circle is the largest?
All three are the same size. You can easily prove this by measuring their diameters. The borders around the three circles confuse your brain—they distract attention from the blue circles. Because the borders are different, the blue circles appear to be unequal.

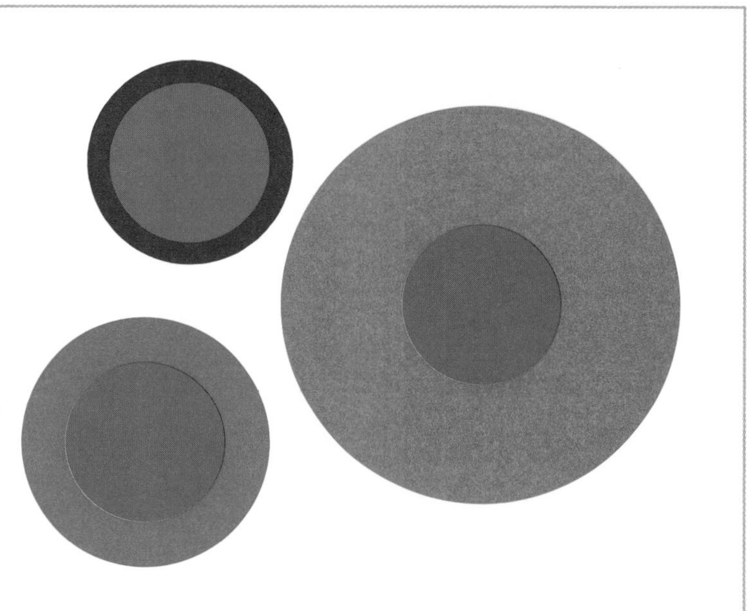

Close your right eye and stare at the cross. Very slowly move the drawing closer to your eyes. At one point, the red dot disappears. This happens when the dot's image falls on part of the eye called the blind spot. This area doesn't send messages to the brain. So the brain guesses, and it fills the space with slanted lines.

Look at the dark squares in this drawing. Do you see dancing gray spots where the white lines cross one another?

The spots aren't really there. You see them because white looks brighter when it's next to a dark color than when it's next to a light color. In the drawing, the white of the lines between the dark squares seems whiter than the white where two lines cross. Now look directly at one of the dancing gray spots. You can't! The spots disappear when you try to look directly at them.

Where is the middle prong attached? The drawing gives conflicting information. The left part of the drawing looks like three pipes. The right part looks like a flat box. Together, the two parts don't make sense. The brain is confused because it can't imagine a three-dimensional object.

Look at the green stripes in this drawing. Are those on the left lighter than those on the right?

They seem to be, but they are actually exactly the same color. Contrast between a color and its background can make the color seem lighter or darker. The green stripes on the left lie against a light orange background. Those on the right lie against a black background.

Are the slanted lines in this drawing parallel to each other or not?

Your brain most likely thinks that the lines aren't parallel—but they are! Check this by laying a ruler along one of the slanted lines; then slide it to each of the other lines.

Your brain is confused by the short "hatch marks" running through the lines. This kind of extra information is called "visual noise."

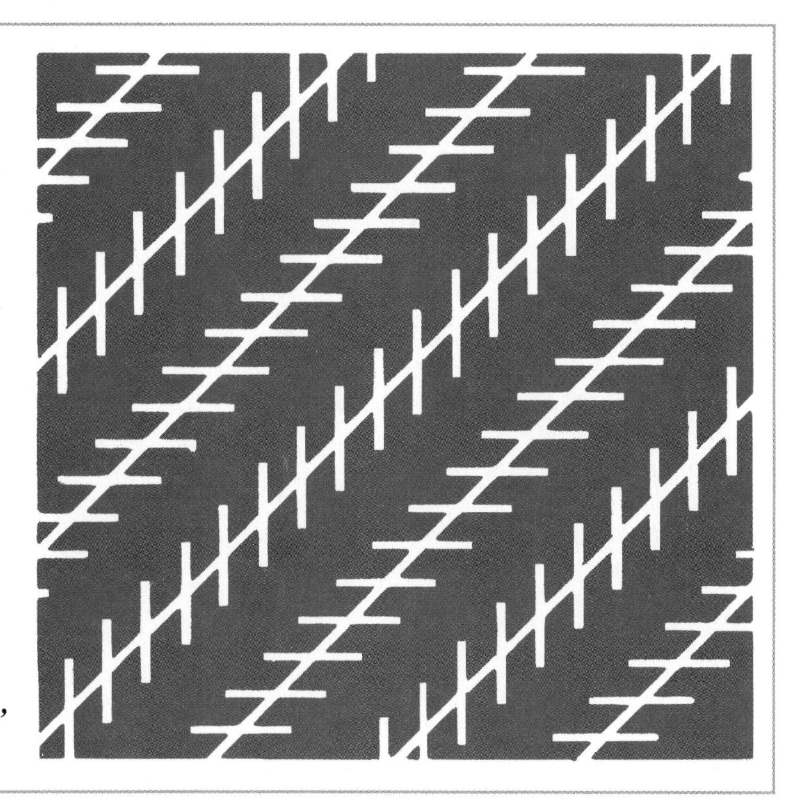

Does this drawing seem to vibrate? It's called the shimmering-star illusion.

The brain sees motion that isn't there. It can't decide if it sees radiating black lines or radiating white lines. It keeps switching from one image to the other.

Flipbooks also give the illusion of motion. You are looking at single pictures. But they flash past your eyes so fast that you "see" motion.

Do you see two faces in profile? Or do you see a wide-topped vase?

It depends on whether your brain interprets the picture as showing two dark objects against a light background—or one light object against a dark background.

Your brain is confused. It can't decide what is background and what is foreground. So it switches back and forth between the two images. You never see both images at the same time—the brain can only make one image at a time.

PINOCCHIO'S NOSE KNOWS

Pinocchio burst into Geppetto's shop.

"Father!" he called out. "Where are you?"

"In my workshop," answered Geppetto.

Pinocchio dropped his schoolbooks and skipped back to his father's workroom. Geppetto was painting something. Pinocchio had to stand on his tiptoes to see what it was.

"What a pretty little girl!" he said.

"It's a puppet, Pinocchio," his father said.

Geppetto lifted the marionette off the workbench and danced her across the floor. He thought she was the prettiest puppet he had ever made.

"May I play with her, Father?" asked Pinocchio.

"No," replied Geppetto. "I made her for Mr. Santos, the puppeteer."

Pinocchio was disappointed. He thought his father had made him a playmate.

Geppetto put on his coat. "I have to go out for an hour, Pinocchio," he said. "Now be a good boy while I'm gone, and don't touch the puppet."

"Yes, Father," answered Pinocchio.

"Well, Pinoke," said Jiminy Cricket. "It's time to do your homework."

"Okay," said Pinocchio. He began to practice his alphabet. But soon he got up.

"What's the matter?" asked Jiminy.

"Oh, nothing," Pinocchio answered. "I just feel like walking around a little." He wandered over to Cleo's goldfish bowl and watched her swim around in circles. He sat down next to Figaro, who was napping, and watched the kitten's whiskers twitch. He watched a cuckoo pop out from a clock on the wall.

Then Pinocchio wandered into Geppetto's workroom. He ran his fingers along the edge of the workbench. He kicked at some wood shavings under the bench. He picked up one of Geppetto's tools and put it down.

"Come on, Pinoke," called Jiminy. "I'll help you finish your homework."

"I'll be right there," said Pinocchio.

But Pinocchio spotted the red-headed puppet. She was so pretty. Father won't mind, he said to himself. So he pulled the puppet off the workbench—and she crashed to the floor in a tangle of strings.

“What’s that?” called Jiminy.

“Oh, nothing,” said Pinocchio nervously. “I just dropped something.”

Pinocchio bent down to pick up the new puppet. One of her arms had come off.

Gripping her close to his chest, Pinocchio looked at the place where her arm was supposed to attach. The end of a string was sticking out from her body. Pinocchio pulled on it until he had enough to tie the arm back on.

“Well, the other arm kind of sticks out,” he said to himself, “but I don’t think Father will notice.”

Then he looked at the puppet’s face. He gasped. The paint hadn’t been dry, and her features had smeared. Pinocchio looked down at his chest. There, on the front of his clothes, was most of the puppet’s face.

“Oh, no!” he said, out loud.

“What’s wrong?” called Jiminy.

“Oh, nothing,” answered Pinocchio. “I just . . . um, have to fix something.”

Pinocchio climbed up on Geppetto's stool. Carefully he repainted the puppet's face.

"There," he said to himself. "She's as good as new." He set the red-headed marionette back on the workbench and went to finish his homework.

When Geppetto returned home later in the day, he found Pinocchio and Jiminy hard at work. He took off his coat and went back to his workroom.

Suddenly Geppetto called out. "Pinocchio! What were you doing while I was gone?"

"My homework, Father," answered Pinocchio.

"Is that all?" Geppetto asked.

"Of course, Father," Pinocchio replied.

He felt a funny feeling on his face, and he heard a little squeak.

Jiminy Cricket gasped. “Pinoke!” he whispered, pointing to Pinocchio’s face.

“Sssh!” hissed Pinocchio.

“Are you sure that was all you did?” asked Geppetto again, coming to the door.

“Yes, Father,” said Pinocchio. He felt another tweak and heard another squeak.

“Pinocchio, look at me,” said Geppetto.

“Pinoke,” Jiminy cried. “Your nose!”

Pinocchio looked down. Then he quickly clapped his hands over his face.

“I don’t think you are telling me the truth,” said Geppetto, shaking his head.

“But I am,” protested Pinocchio. *Pop!* His wooden nose poked through his fingers.

Pinocchio hung his head in shame. “I tried to fix her, Father,” he said.

“You have caused me a lot of extra work,” said Geppetto. “You’ll have to help me fix her.”

So after he had finished his homework, Pinocchio worked far into the night. He scrubbed and sanded until he had cleaned the puppet’s face.

“Well, Pinocchio,” said Geppetto, “you did a good job and you may go to bed now. But I don’t know what we are going to do about your nose.”

Wearily, Pinocchio dragged himself up the stairs. He knew the other children at school would laugh when they saw his nose. He thought about pretending to be sick the next day, so he wouldn’t

have to go to school. But then he remembered. That would be telling a lie, and lying had already got him into enough trouble. He would just have to face everyone. With a huge sigh, he got into bed and went to sleep.

Later that night, Pinocchio woke up. Something was strange. There was a light at his window.

"Jiminy," Pinocchio called. "What's going on?"

Jiminy Cricket rubbed the sleep from his eyes. Then he sat up. "I don't believe it!" he said.

"You should believe it," said a very sweet voice.

"Is it you, Blue Fairy?" asked Pinocchio. "Gosh, I'm so glad to see you."

Then he remembered what had happened to his nose. He tried to hide under the covers.

"I see that you haven't been telling the truth," said the Blue Fairy.

"No, ma'am," said Pinocchio.

"What have you learned?" she asked.

Pinocchio thought. Then he looked at her and said, "It's always better to tell the truth."

"Ma'am," said Jiminy Cricket, "couldn't you do something about his nose?"

"Yes, I should fix that," the fairy said. "He has learned his lesson." She waved her magic wand.

In a flash, Pinocchio's nose went back to its normal size.

"Oh, thank you, Blue Fairy!" he cried.

"You're welcome," she replied. "Now go to sleep and remember —no more lies."

The next morning, Geppetto noticed Pinocchio's nose right away. "What has happened?" he said.

"The Blue Fairy came last night," said Pinocchio, "and she waved her wand, and she fixed my nose, and . . ."

"Yes, yes," said Geppetto, impatiently. "And she gave you a pot of gold, too. Pinocchio, why won't you tell the truth?"

"But that *is* the truth, Father," said the little puppet.

Then Geppetto realized something—Pinocchio's nose wasn't growing. He was telling the truth.

Geppetto smiled. "I guess you have learned your lesson."

"Yes, Father," said Pinocchio. "I have. I will never tell another lie."

Jiminy Cricket made a little squeak. Pinocchio gasped and felt his nose.

"Just joking, Pinoke," chuckled Jiminy.

I'm a small, furry creature with a long tail. Indeed, my tail is longer than my body! I live high in the trees of the forests in South America. I sleep during the day. As dusk falls, I wake up and open my big, round eyes and stretch and yawn. I like to leap from tree to tree and swing on vines—just like Tarzan!
(I'm a night monkey or owl monkey.)

I'm a big bird, and I live in the rain forests of Sumatra, an Indonesian island. On top of my beak is a huge orange horny growth. It looks something like the horn of a large mammal that lives in Asia and Africa. I am a noisy bird, and I use my horn to amplify my call—which sounds like "GR-RONK!"
(I'm a rhinoceros hornbill.)

WHAT'S IN A NAME?

You have found an animal never before seen by people. How do you choose its name? One part of the name, as in "blackbird," may describe the animal's color. Where the animal lives may be part of

My name tells you the continent I live near and my habitat. The continent lies in the Southern Hemisphere between the Pacific and Indian oceans. The habitat is made up of salty water. Many of my relatives live on land; these slow-moving critters are pests in people's gardens. But the only people who see me *are divers.*
(I'm an Australian sea slug.)

I belong to a certain group of beetles. My neck is so long that I have been named after a tall mammal of the African plains. (You've probably seen one in a zoo.) My head is rather long, too, thanks to a large snout. I live on Madagascar, an island off the coast of Africa. And I'm a male. My female relatives don't have long necks.
(I'm a giraffe weevil or snout beetle.)

the name, too—the "European blackbird." Many names describe unusual features. For instance, there's a fish that has a long snout shaped like a tube, which it uses to suck up food. It's called the "tube-mouthed fish." Look at the animals on these pages and read about them. Do you think their names fit them?

Magnificent Marbles!

The story is told of a boy named Zeke, who once took his marbles to the playground. There he was challenged to a game of marbles. Zeke lost the game. Even worse, following the rules of the playground, the winner got to keep the loser's marbles. So Zeke gave up his prize possessions, and he ran home in tears. "You look like you've lost your best friend," said his father. "No," Zeke sobbed, "I've lost my marbles!" "Losing your marbles" has come to mean more than just that. It also means "losing your senses," as if you had gone mad. Perhaps poor Zeke had indeed "lost his marbles" in both meanings of the term.

Marbles have been used by people for hundreds of years. Ancient peoples used small stones, sheep's knucklebones, and even tiny nuts as marbles. Today, marbles are usually made of glass—these are called "glassies." There are also marbles made of agate (called "aggies"), marbles that are steel or brass ball bearings (called "steelies"), and marbles made from fired clay (called "crockies"). Some marbles are as small as peas, and others as large as golf balls. But most are somewhere in between, about the size of a gumball. Marbles are used in dozens of games. They are also collected for their beauty. Above all, marbles are fun.

People in countries around the world call playing with marbles many different names. In the United States, it's called "marbles" or "immies" or "mibs." English, Irish, and Scottish kids play "boss" or "taw" or "span." In parts of Africa it's called "jorrah," and in Brazil it's called "gude." But while marble playing has different names, and there are hundreds of variations, there really are only three basic kinds of games:

Tournament of Marbles

Every June, in Wildwood, New Jersey, the National Marbles Tournament is held for players ages 8 to 14. About 75 boys and girls participate in the five-day event. They compete in a popular marbles game called Ringer. Boys challenge boys, and girls challenge girls, until two national champions are crowned. Each of the two champs wins a trophy and a $2,000 scholarship. In 1993, the tournament celebrated its 70th anniversary.

1. Hole games. Marbles are shot into, out of, or near holes in the ground or in boxes.

2. Chase games. Players shoot their marbles at opponents' marbles as they follow a winding course.

3. Enclosure games. Players shoot their marbles at other marbles within an enclosure such as a circle or a square.

Even if you don't play marble games, it's great fun to collect these beautiful, smooth, shiny little spheres. They are made with an amazing variety of colors and designs. Some marbles have no pattern running through them—hold them up to the light and they seem to glow. And some very rare ones are clear glass with a tiny figure inside—perhaps the image of a well-known historical figure.

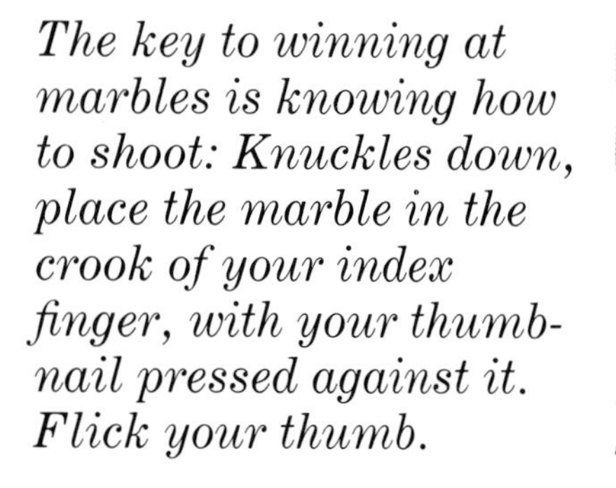

The key to winning at marbles is knowing how to shoot: Knuckles down, place the marble in the crook of your index finger, with your thumbnail pressed against it. Flick your thumb.

Other Uses for Marbles

- *Chinese Checkers is a game in which marbles are the pieces. They are moved from hole to hole on a board as each player tries to outwit the others. (You can see two versions of the game in the photo above.)*
- *Have you ever shaken an aerosol can and heard something clicking inside? It's a marble, and it's used to stir up the contents of the can. This helps the contents come out more easily when you press the button.*
- *In fish hatcheries, you will see marbles on the bottom of spawning pools. They help increase the number of fish eggs that are laid.*

But most marbles are decorated with delicate swirls or tiny cloudlike patterns. They come in every imaginable shade—splashes of rose and pink, spirals of emerald, flashes of orange and yellow, pale blues and dusky browns, sunset purples, and blacks like midnight. Why not start a collection of your own!

TEATIME

"Slow down, Abu!" whispered Aladdin. "You don't have to stuff your face!"

Princess Jasmine smiled and said, "You live in the palace now, Abu. You'll always have plenty of food to eat."

Abu looked up from the platter of fruit and watched Jasmine sip a glass of mint tea. Then he picked up a cup and imitated the princess. He raised his pinky finger, pursed his lips, and took a teensy sip of hot tea. But the tea was too hot for the little monkey. Abu dropped the cup and grabbed a melon. Aladdin and Jasmine laughed as Abu swallowed huge mouthfuls of the cool, juicy fruit.

Jasmine put down her glass and sighed.

"What's the matter, Jasmine?" Aladdin asked.

"Oh, nothing," she replied. "It's another hot, sunny day. And we're sitting here drinking mint tea."

"So?" Aladdin said.

"So," Jasmine explained, "*every* day in Agrabah is hot and sunny. And *every* day we sit here and drink mint tea. Oh, how I would love a change!"

Aladdin asked, "A change in what?"

"Anything—everything!" Jasmine exclaimed. "The weather, the view . . . even the tea!"

Aladdin smiled and whistled. The Magic Carpet heard him and flew out to the royal couple. "Come on, Princess," he said, standing on the carpet. "I know just the place for a change in everything! You too, Abu!" Abu grabbed an armful of fruit and jumped on the carpet.

Up over Agrabah they flew as the Magic Carpet sped eastward. They rode through the clouds for hundreds and hundreds of miles.

The Magic Carpet finally set them down next to a wooden building high in the mountains of an exotic land.

"Welcome to the Hot Springs Teahouse, Princess," Aladdin said as he stepped off the Magic Carpet.

"And this must be snow!" cried Jasmine, holding out her hands, catching the cold, white, lacy snowflakes that floated down from the sky. The princess had only read about snow in storybooks.

Aladdin smiled, packed a snowball in his hands, and threw it at Abu.

"Eeeck!" screeched Abu. The little monkey scampered inside the teahouse. Aladdin laughed.

"Oh, look!" Jasmine cried, pointing to Aladdin's laughter, visible in the freezing air.

“I can see your laugh! And mine! It looks like puffs of white, fluffy smoke!”

Soon they went inside. The teahouse was warm and cozy. The Magic Carpet had already curled up in a corner to nap.

Aladdin and Jasmine drank hot green tea out of tiny china cups. Jasmine enjoyed the delicate flavor of the tea. “This is a wonderful change, Aladdin,” she said happily.

But Abu was not happy. Not only was it cold and wet outside, there was no fruit or cake to eat! Abu climbed up into the rafters. He looked out at snow-covered mountains and chattered angrily to himself.

After a warming cup of tea, Aladdin and Jasmine went outside to play in the snow. Together they worked on a snow sculpture that looked just like someone they knew. "It's the Genie, all right!" Jasmine exclaimed.

Meanwhile, Abu looked out the teahouse window and saw a monkey looking at him! The monkey smiled and scampered onto the next tree branch. Curious, Abu followed him. The monkey leaped from tree to tree, away from the teahouse and into the forest, with Abu right behind him.

Aladdin added some more snow to the snow genie's belly and gave it a final pat. "Done!"

"This was so much fun!" said the princess when they went inside the teahouse. "Thank you, Aladdin. I guess I'm ready to go home now."

"Your wish is my command, Princess," Aladdin said with a bow. Then he whistled for the Magic Carpet. "All we need is Abu, and we'll be back in Agrabah in no time."

Aladdin turned to look for his pet monkey. "Abu! Abu, time to go home!" he called. But Abu didn't appear.

"Where could he be?" wondered Aladdin. He and Jasmine looked all over the teahouse. The Magic Carpet looked, too. They couldn't find Abu anywhere.

Finally Jasmine said, "Abu's nowhere in here. Maybe he went outside."

Together they searched outside the teahouse, but they still couldn't find Abu. Aladdin walked by the snow genie and said, "Boy, do I wish the real genie could help us!"

Aladdin looked past the snow sculpture and saw several strange-looking monkeys sitting near it. Much to his surprise, one of the monkeys was wearing Abu's hat!

"Follow that monkey!" cried Aladdin.

Aladdin's shout startled the monkeys and they scampered away. Riding the Magic Carpet, the royal couple followed the monkeys up the mountainside.

"Look!" gasped Jasmine. Abu's vest was hanging on the branch of a tree. The Magic Carpet paused and Jasmine picked up the vest. "Oh, dear!" she cried. "He must be freezing!"

At last the monkeys stopped. They leaped out of the trees and into a pond. Warm water splashed up on Aladdin and Jasmine. "This must be the hot springs that give the teahouse its name," Aladdin said.

A whole troop of snow monkeys was sitting in the water and laughing.

And there was Abu, surrounded by the monkey troop. He was standing on a large rock in the middle of the pool and making all the monkeys laugh. Aladdin and Jasmine laughed, too.

"He's imitating the Genie!" Jasmine exclaimed, as Abu did his best version of their favorite big, blue guy.

Aladdin chuckled and said, "Come on, Abu. Time to go home."

Abu said good-bye to his Japanese cousins, grabbed his hat and vest, and jumped on the Magic Carpet.

They all waved to the monkeys as the Magic Carpet left Japan and headed back to Agrabah.

Nearing the palace, Aladdin said, "That was great! And we even managed to find Abu without the Genie's help!"

"What about our snow genie?" Jasmine reminded him.

"Well, *almost* without a genie's help," Aladdin admitted.

First Kid Chelsea Clinton with her father, President Bill Clinton.

Imagine being accompanied by Secret Service agents and followed by reporters everywhere you go—to school, to a friend's home, to the movies, to a store. That's just one of the changes that 12-year-old Chelsea Clinton had to get used to when her father, Bill Clinton, became president of the United States in January 1993. Like the children and grandchildren of many previous presidents, she quickly learned that life as America's "First Kid" is very exciting—but it may have some drawbacks, too.

Chelsea is the newest in a long line of First Kids. Let's take a look at some of the others. Abraham Lincoln's sons Willie and Tad were 10 and 8 when they moved into the White House in 1861. They threw parties, staged shows, and roughhoused so much that the staff feared they would wreck the place. When Willie died the next year, his parents were grief stricken. Tad became the focus of his father's affection. And although the Civil War was raging, Lincoln often took the time to help his son with his reading.

After Franklin Delano Roosevelt took office in 1933, two of his grandchildren, 6-year-old Eleanor (Sistie) and 2-year-old Curtis (Buzzie), moved into the White House. With its indoor pool and private movie theater, the White House was lots of fun for them.

John F. Kennedy's daughter, Caroline, was 3, and his son, John, Jr., was just two months old when he took office in 1961. The press had a great time writing stories about the Kennedy kids. As "John-John" grew older, he liked

to crawl around the floor in the Oval Office.

Amy Carter was 9 when her father, Jimmy Carter, took office in 1977. Secret Service agents went everywhere with her, and reporters followed her around. To get some privacy, she built a tree house on the White House grounds to have a place where she could just be by herself.

Chelsea Clinton turned 13 on February 27, 1993, just a month after her father, Bill Clinton, was sworn in as the 42nd president. Chelsea easily settled into her new eighth-grade class at the Sidwell Friends private school. Drama and environmental science were among the subjects she studied. And she found a good spot to do her homework—the presidential study next to the Oval Office. Chelsea is a good student and hopes to be a scientist or an astronaut someday. She also likes to read, talk on the phone, and spend time with her friends.

Chelsea moved to Washington, D.C., settled into her new school, and joined the school soccer team.

Although her parents are often busy with their new duties, there is still time for favorite family activities—playing cards, watching videos, and riding bikes. Of course, wherever Chelsea goes, Secret Service agents and reporters tag along. But Chelsea is determined to make her life as First Kid as normal as possible.

Nifty Notecards!

These nifty notecards are easy to make—and lots of fun. All you need are some inexpensive materials and your imagination! Gather together flat-backed buttons, feathers, sequins, pearls, pieces of felt, white glue, and folded sheets of construction paper. First decide on a design. Next cut out shapes from the felt. Then arrange the felt shapes and the other decorations on the front side of the paper. Glue all the pieces down.

After the glue has dried, add any finishing touches. For example, on a button-face, use felt-tip pens to add eyes, a nose, and a mouth. You can also add a border around the card. All done? Then it's time to write your message!

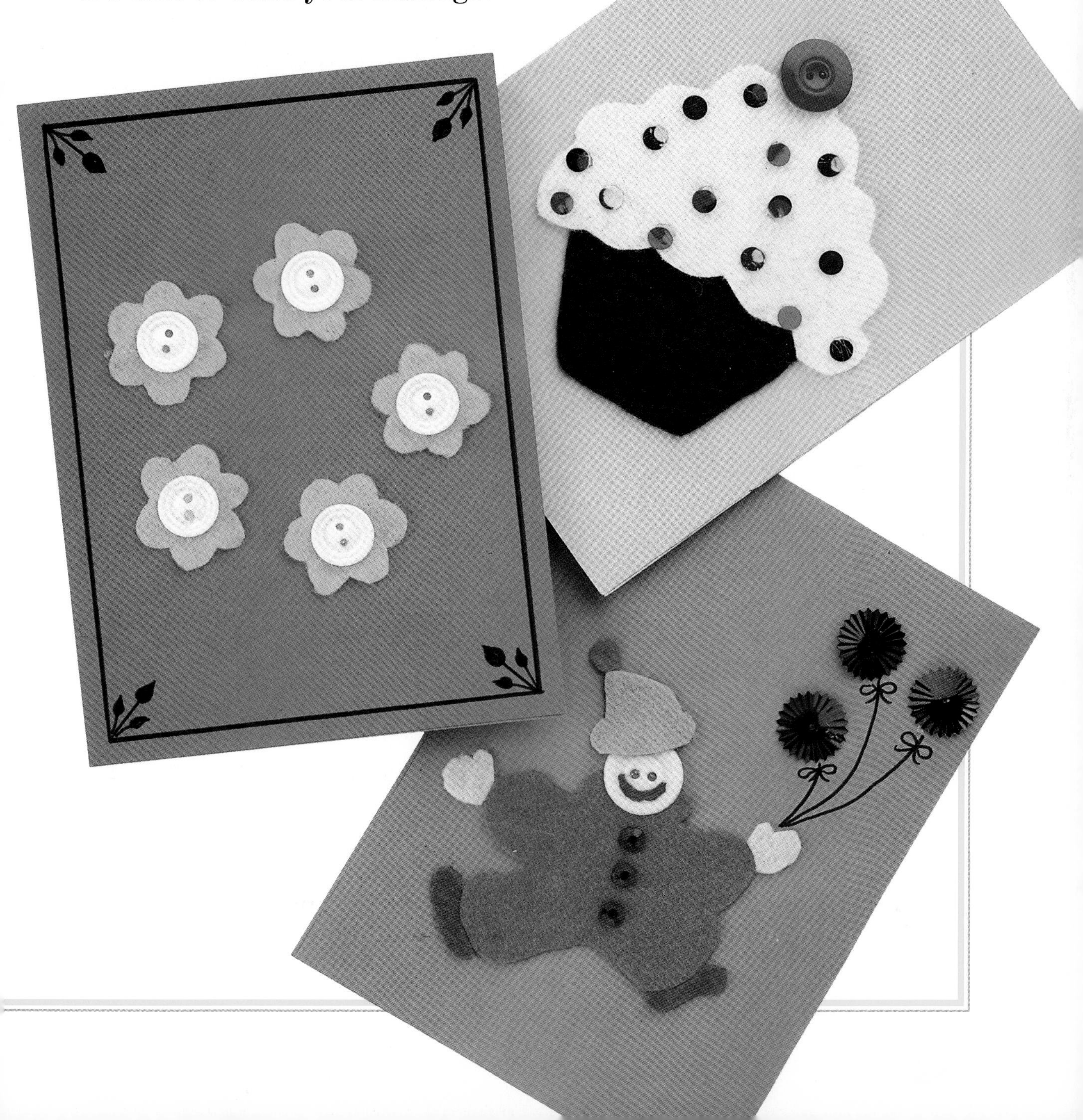

Jon and the Three Wishes

Once upon a time there was a young man named Jon. He worked very hard on his farm. But no matter how hard he worked, he was still very poor.

One evening Jon was coming home from a hard day in his field. All of a sudden, he saw a strange glow. He tied his plowhorse to a tree and went to look at it.

The glow was coming from the middle of a ring of bushes. Peeking over them, Jon saw a wonderful sight. There were many tiny people, all dressed in velvet green coats and bright red caps. They were sitting at tables having a feast.

Some of the little people picked up pipes and fiddles and began to play a lively tune. All the others danced happily in the moonlight. Jon tapped his foot in time to the music. Before he knew it, he was clapping his hands. But when the little people heard him, everything vanished—the tables, the food, the dancers, and the musicians.

"It must have been a fairy feast," Jon thought to himself. He had heard people say that fairies had been seen there before.

As Jon started to leave, he saw a light in one of the bushes. He bent down to see better and found a fairy caught in the brambles by her long golden hair.

The more the lovely little fairy pulled and tugged, the more she became entangled.

"Poor thing," thought Jon. He pulled out his knife and cut her free.

"Oh, thank you," the fairy said. "If you had not freed me, I don't know what would have happened to me!"

"It was nothing," said Jon shyly. "I would have done the same for anyone."

"Well, I am very grateful," answered the fairy. "And as your reward, I will give you three wishes."

She handed three of her golden hairs to Jon. "Hold one up at night when the moon is bright and make a wish. I will grant it." Then the fairy vanished.

When Jon got home, he hid the golden hairs under his straw mattress. The next day he barely remembered his adventure. Soon he forgot it altogether, which is what usually happens when people meet fairies.

Now as it happened, the king of the land was looking for a husband for his daughter, the kind and beautiful Princess Cassie. Soon everyone in the kingdom knew about it.

The king loved his daughter very much, and he wanted to find the perfect young man for her. So he decided that the man would have to pass three difficult tests, one for strength, one for courage, and one for honesty.

Knights from far and wide came to try the test of strength. But no one was able to chop down the giant tree that grew outside the castle wall. Its trunk was as thick as ten men. And its branches spread over much of the land.

Jon watched as one knight after another failed the test. "If only I could win," he thought. "But I'm only a humble farmer. I don't have the strength of a knight."

Then one day Jon was working in the field, and he saw the princess out walking. She was very beautiful. Jon stared at her long golden hair.

Then he remembered. "The little fairy's three wishes!" he said to himself. "They can help me!"

That night when the moon was out, Jon held up one of the golden strands. "Help me cut down the giant tree and marry the princess," he said.

He waited quietly to see what would happen next.

Then there was a flash, and a magic axe lay in Jon's hand. Its blade was made of the strongest metal.

The next morning he went to the tree. He swung the enchanted axe with all his strength. There was a great crack and groan. Then came a crash that shook the ground for miles around. The giant tree had fallen.

Jon was summoned before the king, who praised his strength. But Jon wasn't listening. His eyes were on the fair Cassie. She was looking at Jon. It was plain to see that the two young people were falling in love.

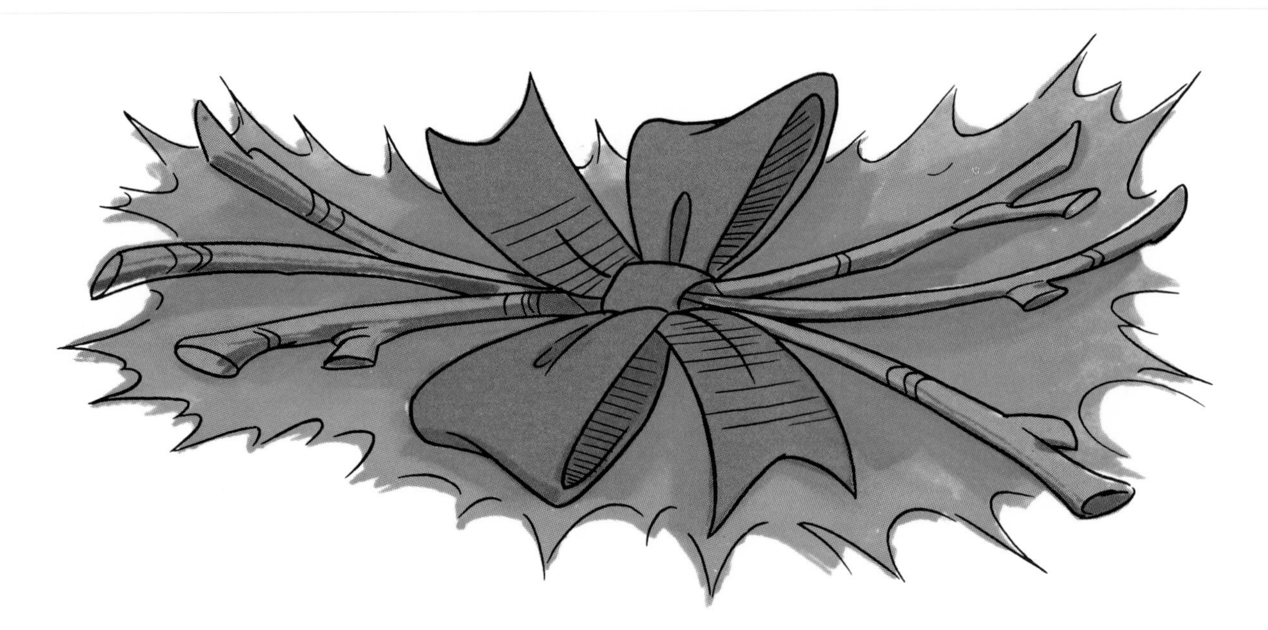

"Now your next test will be to see how courageous you are," announced the king. "To do this, you must spend the night in the haunted wood, deep in the forest. I will ride to the forest the next morning. If you are still there, you will have proved that you are very brave."

When the princess heard this, she fainted and had to be carried from the room. She knew that no one had ever spent the night in the haunted wood and lived. And she cared so much for Jon that she could not stand to think of him being in danger.

That evening as the moon rose high, Jon held up the second of the fairy's golden hairs. "Help me spend the night in the haunted wood so I can win the hand of the princess."

Again there was a flash, and Jon was holding a fairy charm. It was three twigs tied together with a red ribbon. One twig was from an oak tree. Another twig was from an ash tree. And the third twig was from a thorn tree. Jon tucked the charm carefully under his arm and went to the haunted wood.

The wood was a dark, foul-smelling place. Weeds grew wild. Thick moss hung from the trees, blocking out the moonlight. Strange sounds could be heard.

But Jon didn't feel frightened. He had the fairy charm, after all. So he lay down, curled up under a tree, and immediately fell fast asleep.

When he awoke the next morning, the weeds and moss were gone. He heard the birds chirping and saw sunlight shining through the trees. The haunted wood was now a beautiful wood, with flowers growing everywhere.

Jon sat down to wait for the king.

When the king found Jon, he could hardly believe his eyes. He was surprised that Jon had been able to live through a night in the haunted wood. And not only that—he had also gotten rid of the evil spirits!

"You have done far better than I expected," said the astonished

king. "Come to the castle tomorrow for your final test, the test of honesty."

That night John held up the last golden hair. "Help me win the test of honesty so I can marry the princess," he said.

This time the fairy appeared to Jon and handed him a small cake.

"Whoever eats this can only see and say the truth," she said. Then she vanished.

The next morning Jon stood before the king with the small cake in his hand. The princess stood next to her father, smiling. She could hardly wait for Jon to pass the last test so the two could be married.

"Now for the test of honesty," said the king. "Answer me this:

Did you pass the tests of strength and courage all on your own, without any help?"

Jon was naturally a truthful person. He didn't need the help of the magic cake to tell the king about the fairy, the axe, and the charm, so he replied, "No, I didn't."

"Ha!" cried the king with a sly smile. "That disqualifies you, and you cannot marry my daughter!"

The princess began to cry. But suddenly the king saw the fairy cake in Jon's hand. For some reason, he couldn't help himself. He grabbed the cake and ate it.

A strange look came over the king's face. Then he, too, began to weep. "I am a lonely and selfish old man," he sobbed. "I was afraid my daughter would marry and leave me all alone. So I made up a contest that no one could possibly win. But now I know how wrong I was."

"Jon, you are a strong, courageous, and truthful young man. Most important of all, my daughter loves you and you love her. I will be very happy if you marry. "

Not long after that, Jon and Princess Cassie were married. And since Jon had no kingdom of his own, he came to live at the castle. The king was never lonely. In fact, all three of them lived happily ever after.

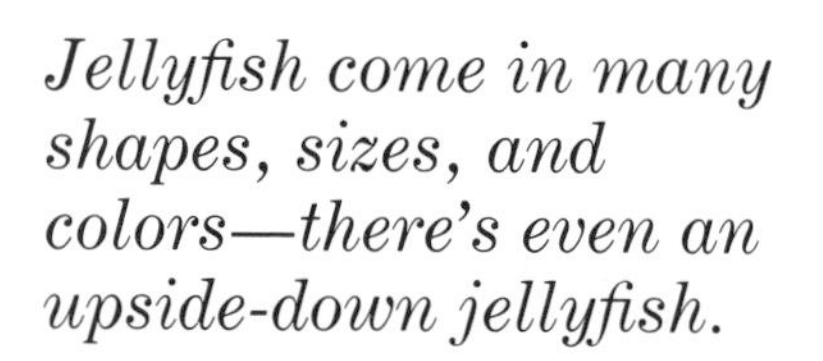

Jellyfish come in many shapes, sizes, and colors—there's even an upside-down jellyfish.

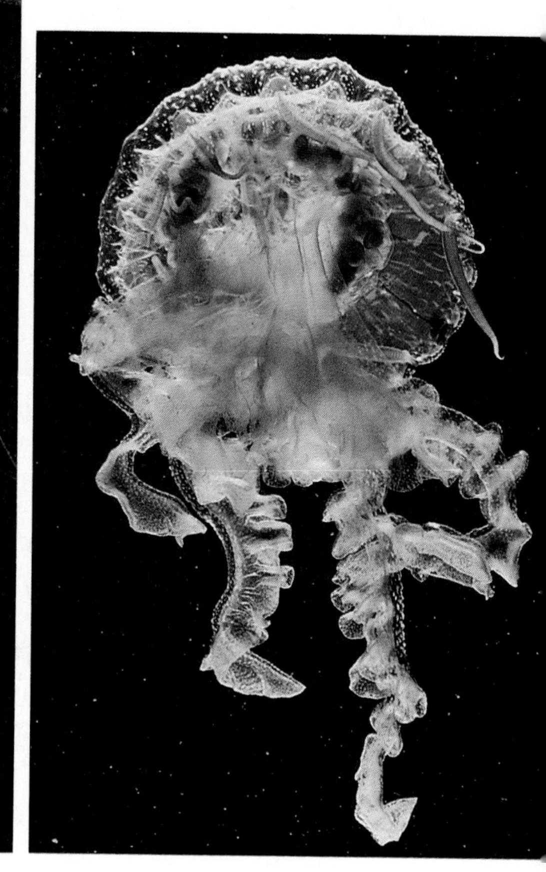

Jellyfish: Umbrellas of the Sea

Washed up on a beach, a jellyfish looks like a blob of slime. But floating in the water, its translucent body shimmers with a thousand colors. In fact, jellyfish are among the world's most beautiful creatures. They are also among the oldest forms of life—more than 650 million years old.

There are hundreds of different kinds of jellyfish—no one is sure how many. They are found in all the waters of the ocean, from the tropics to the Arctic seas. Some types swim and feed in shallow waters along beaches and river mouths. Others live in the ocean depths, as far down as 2,000 feet.

Jellyfish don't look like fish—and in fact they aren't fish. They are related to sea anemones and corals. A jellyfish is a very simple animal. Its body is 95 percent water. It has no bones, heart, brain, or nervous system. But it does have nerve cells that are sensitive to touch and eyespots that detect light.

Most jellyfish have a body

that is in the shape of an umbrella or a bell. It has just two cell layers. In between the two layers is a mass of jellylike material that stiffens the body and helps the animal float.

Jellyfish move through the water by jet propulsion. To go forward, the jellyfish contracts its bell, forcing water out behind and pushing itself up or ahead.

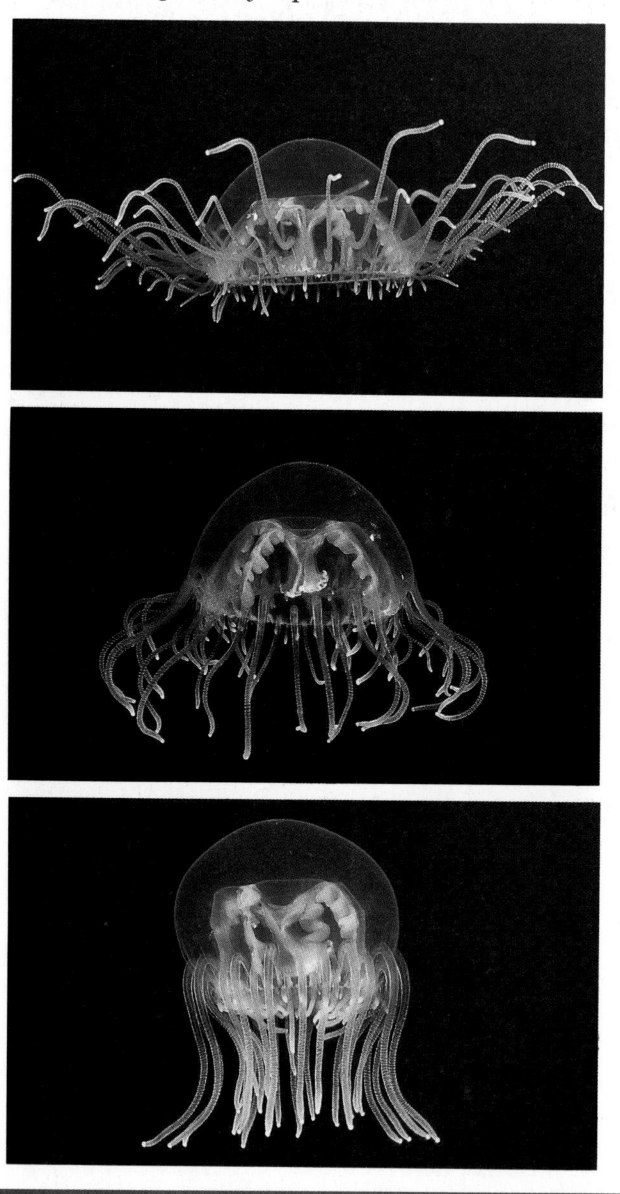

Within the body is the jellyfish's stomach. As the jellyfish swims along, its mouth and long tentacles hang down from the underside of its body. Jellyfish use the tentacles to catch prey. Anything that touches the tentacles—often small fish—gets a poisonous sting. Then the prey is swept into the jellyfish's mouth and digested.

Although they share the same simple body structure, jellyfish come in a truly remarkable variety of sizes and shapes. The largest jellyfish have umbrellas that measure as much as 7 feet across, and their tentacles

Deadly Jellies

Many jellyfish can deliver painful stings—and some stings can be highly poisonous. So it's smart ***not to touch a jellyfish,*** *in or out of the water. A jellyfish's sting is delivered by special cells that are like tiny capsules of poison. These cells can release their poison even after the jellyfish is dead. The Portuguese man-of-war (above) is probably the most dangerous jellyfish in North American waters. Its sting can cause blisters and may even be fatal to people.*

may be more than 100 feet long. The smallest jellyfish are a mere half inch in size. Jellyfish also come in many colors. But most are partly or completely transparent. And many are bioluminescent—they contain chemicals that give off an eerie, glowing light.

There is still much to learn about jellyfish. Perhaps you can visit an aquarium and learn for yourself about these mysterious marine creatures.

This young man in Clarksville, Missouri, stands chest-deep in the floodwaters that engulfed the town during the Great Flood of 1993.

THE GREAT FLOOD OF '93

Trees were uprooted. Houses were swept away. Entire towns and millions of acres of farmland were submerged. It was the Great Flood of 1993. And for much of the summer, the terrible floods left parts of nine Midwestern states—Illinois, Iowa, Kansas, Minnesota, Missouri, Nebraska, North Dakota, South Dakota, and Wisconsin—under water.

To understand how this happened, we need to know about the longest river in the United States: the mighty Mississippi. The Mississippi River acts as the country's main drainage system. Rivers in 31 states feed into it.

The area drained by the Mississippi and its tributaries includes some of the finest farmland in the United States—especially in the broad, flat river valleys of the Midwest. But these valleys are part of the floodplain of the river system. Heavy winter snows and spring rains normally cause water levels to rise along these rivers. If the levels rise high enough, the rivers overflow their banks and water pours out onto the floodplain. Over the years, people have built floodwalls and levees to keep the water within the river banks, and reservoirs to capture overflow.

Entire towns were submerged by the flood. And as streets turned into mini-rivers, families piled into rowboats to get around.

The chain of events that led to the Great Flood of 1993 began late in 1992, when the upper Mississippi region had an unusually wet fall. That was followed by heavy winter snows and a very wet spring. By June, the soil was heavy with water. Then came another unusual weather pattern, which brought torrential rains. The soil, already soaked, couldn't absorb the new rain. So the water ran into the rivers, and the rivers rose.

As the rivers began to break out of their banks, regions that weren't protected by floodwalls or levees went under water. But even areas that were protected by levees weren't safe. In town after town, people worked heroically around the clock, trying to raise and reinforce the levees with sandbags. In many cases their

Flood Control

A floodplain is land that borders a river and may be covered by floodwaters. Because floodplains have rich soil, people often move to these areas to farm. Then towns grow up.

People living in floodplain areas have built levees to keep the river waters from overflowing their banks, and reservoirs to capture the overflow.

When water levels rise, levees usually contain the river. But if levels rise high enough, rivers burst through the levees, and the water pours out onto the floodplain.

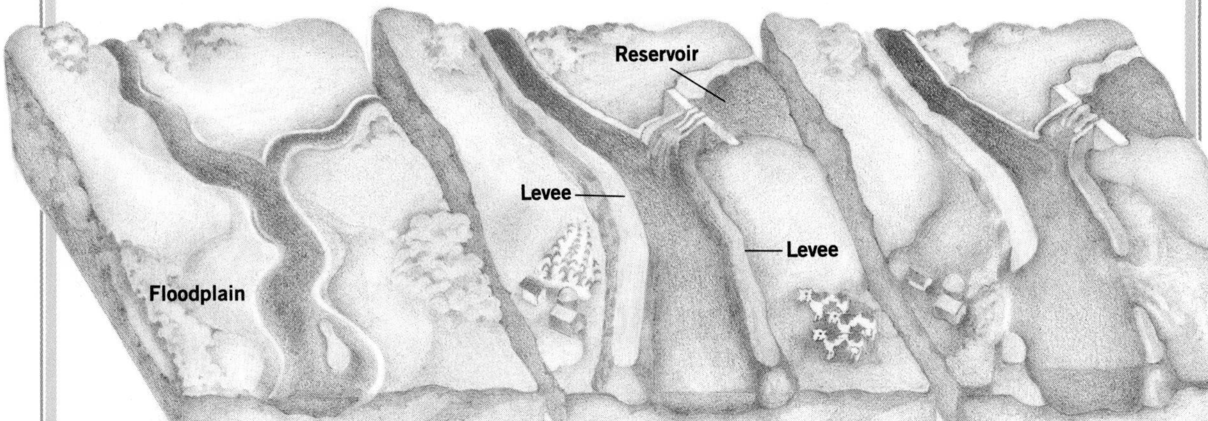

People worked heroically to reinforce levees with sandbags.

efforts paid off, and homes and other buildings were saved. But sometimes they worked in vain. In many towns the floods broke through the levees, putting streets under many feet of water.

Highways and railroad lines were washed away. Bridges, roads, and buildings were damaged. Electricity was knocked out. Water supplies were contaminated. Houses were coated with mud. The flooding caused 50 deaths and drove some 70,000 people from their homes. It resulted in billions of dollars in damage to property and crops.

By September, the waters began to fall. People went back to their homes to repair the flood damage, and life slowly returned to normal. But it was clear that the Great Flood of 1993 would be talked about for many years to come.

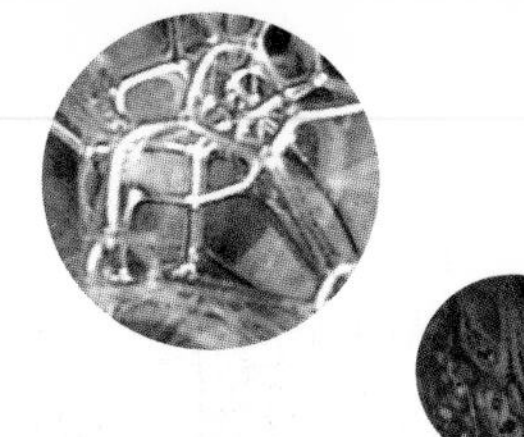

Bubbles of Fun

Bubbles are beautiful. They may last only a few moments, but in the right hands they can do some amazing things—especially these bubbles, which were made with a mixture of liquid soap, glycerine, and water.

Rolling Bubbles

What is a bubble? It is air wrapped in a thin film of liquid. And it usually pops when it touches something. But this girl can roll bubbles back and forth on her string loop. How? The loop is soaked in the special bubble mixture, and the soap film on it becomes part of the bubble.

A Bubble Arch

How did these two children get inside the bubble arch without popping it? It was easy—the bubble expert in the center formed the arch around them. The kids are standing on platforms in large pans of special bubble mixture. The bubble expert simply lifted a hoop from one pan and swept it over both children to the other pan.

Easy Does It

Here's a closer look at how a person can be put inside a bubble. The boy carefully sweeps a hoop loaded with soapy bubble mixture over the girl's head. He must be sure that the bubble doesn't touch his or her clothing—or it will pop! The slightest contact with any dry surface, no matter how soft the surface, is all that it takes to break a bubble.

A Bubble Chain

This expert made a bubble chain by blowing a long bubble and closing off sections as they formed. Tricks like this take a lot of practice. The people who can do it know a lot about the science of bubbles —which is called "bubble-ology."

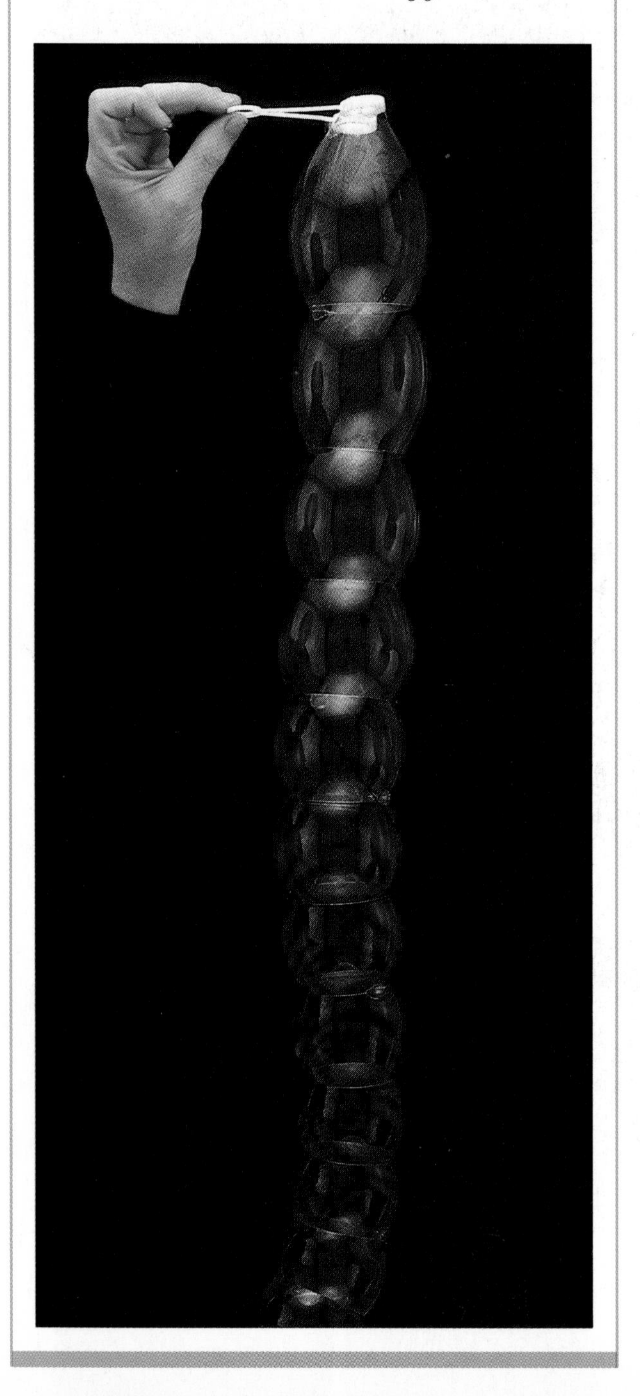

Bubble Coaster

These boys are using a giant string loop to make giant bubbles. They first soaked the string in special bubble mixture. Then, by moving the loop through the air, they were able to get this strange effect. The soap and glycerine in the bubble mixture reduce evaporation, so that the bubble lasts longer. These ingredients also make the bubble-forming film stretchy, so that the bubbles can be giant-sized.

Bubble Squares

We usually think of bubbles as round, but they can be many other shapes. In this picture, the bubble in the center is a cube. Its flat sides and squared-off corners are formed by the outer bubbles, which press against it. Blowing bubbles inside bubbles is another fancy trick that takes a lot of practice.

I LOVE TO SING!

There's nothing quite as wonderful in all the world as song.
Especially when I can get my friends to sing along.
But even when I'm all alone a song is company.
I sing of places far away that I can't wait to see.

I sing about my dreams and know
that they'll come true someday.
And when the doubts and fears creep in,
a song shoos them away.
Sometimes I find it hard to say
the thoughts inside my head,
But then I think of music,
and I sing my thoughts instead.

Sometimes I feel like I'll just burst,
and I run off to hide,
'Cause no one seems to understand
the way I feel inside.
But when I sing, my spirits lift.
It never takes that long
Because there's something magical
inside of every song!